Garfield

Here We Go Again

JIM DAVIS

RAVETTE BOOKS

First published by Ravette Books Limited 1986
Reprinted 1986, 1987
This edition first published 1988

Printed and bound in Great Britain
for Ravette Books Limited,
3 Glenside Estate, Star Road, Partridge Green,
Horsham, Sussex RH13 8RA
by Cox & Wyman Ltd, Reading

ISBN 0 948456 10 8

10-8   JIM DAVIS

THERE ARE HUGS
AND THERE ARE HUGS

BUT, THERE ARE NO HUGS
LIKE BEAR HUGS

© 1985 United Feature Syndicate, Inc.

© 1985 United Feature Syndicate, Inc.

© 1985 United Feature Syndicate, Inc.

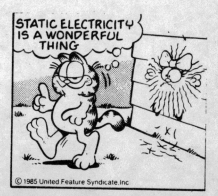

JPM DAVPS   2-5

© 1985 United Feature Syndicate, Inc.

© 1985 United Feature Syndicate,Inc

© 1985 United Feature Syndicate, Inc

THE LONE RANGER HAS TONTO,
THE GREEN HORNET HAS KATO,
AND BATMAN HAS ROBIN.
THE CAPED AVENGER NEEDS A
SIDEKICK TOO

8-27   JIM DAVIS

THEN AGAIN,
I MAY GO THIS
A CAPPELLA

© 1985 United Feature Syndicate, Inc.

© 1985 United Feature Syndicate, Inc.

I FELL ASLEEP ON MY TENNIS RACKET, OKAY?!

OH

© 1985 United Feature Syndicate, Inc.

GET RID
OF THE
DOG!

© 1985 United Feature Syndicate, Inc.

© 1985 United Feature Syndicate,Inc.

© 1985 United Feature Syndicate, inc.

THAT SUN IS PRETTY STRONG TODAY, POOKY. A GUY COULD BURN IF HE'S NOT CAREFUL

6-12 JIM DAVIS

HEY, GARFIELD, HERE'S AN ARTICLE ABOUT A GUY WHO THOUGHT HE COULD FLY BY WEARING A CAPE AND JUMPING OFF A BUILDING

5-30

JIM DAVIS

THEY SCRAPED HIM OFF FIFTH AVENUE WITH A PUTTY KNIFE. I GUESS HE LEARNED HIS LESSON

© 1985 United Feature Syndicate Inc

YEAH, HE DIDN'T BELIEVE

6-1

© 1985 United Feature Syndicate, Inc.

BOING!

© 1985 United Feature Syndicate, Inc.

JIM DAVIS

YOU SHOULD WARN
ME WHEN YOU PUT IN
THE SCREEN DOOR!

5-14

5-16

THAT'S A PRETTY FUNKY DANCE, GARFIELD. SHOW ME HOW YOU DO IT

© 1985 United Feature Syndicate, Inc.

FIRST, FIND A BUR IN YOUR SANDBOX

JIM DAVIS

© 1985 United Feature Syndicate, Inc.

ARE YOU ASHAMED OF YOUR NEW BED, GARFIELD?

WHAT GIVES YOU THAT IDEA?

JPM DAVPS

10-16

© 1985 United Feature Syndicate, Inc.

CLICK

© 1985 United Feature Syndicate, Inc.

JIM DAVIS

© 1985 United Feature Syndicate, Inc.

JIM DAVIS

© 1985 United Feature Syndicate,Inc

UNNNGH!

JIM DAVIS

JIM DAVIS

© 1985 United Feature Syndicate, Inc.

4-16

© 1985 United Feature Syndicate, Inc.

OTHER GARFIELD BOOKS IN THIS SERIES

LANDSCAPE SERIES

COLOUR TV SPECIALS

Here Comes Garfield	£2.95
Garfield On The Town	£2.95
Garfield In The Rough	£2.95
Garfield In Disguise	£2.95
Garfield In Paradise	£2.95
Garfield Goes To Hollywood	£2.95
A Garfield Christmas	£2.95

COLOUR TREASURIES

The Second Garfield Treasury	£5.95
The Third Garfield Treasury	£5.95
The Fourth Garfield Treasury	£5.95
Garfield A Weekend Away	£4.95

All these books are available at your local bookshop or newsagent or can be ordered direct from the publisher. Just tick the titles you require and fill in the form below. Prices and availability subject to change without notice.

Ravette Books Limited, 3 Glenside Estate, Star Road, Partridge Green, Horsham, West Sussex RH13 8RA

Please send a cheque or postal order, and allow the following for postage and packing. UK: Pocket-books and TV Specials – 45p for one book plus 20p for the second book and 15p for each additional book. Landscape Series – 45p for one book plus 30p for each additional book. Treasuries and A Weekend Away – 85p for one book plus 60p for each additional book.

Name ....

Address ....

....